The Evidence of Things Not Seen

Reflections on Faith, Science, and Economics

Vernon L. Smith

With a response by Lenore T. Ealy

Foreword by Samuel Gregg

D1592701

ACTONINSTITUTE

ISBN 978-1-942503-62-0

Cover image: The grand-design spiral galaxy Messier 74 as photographed by the Hubble Space Telescope. NASA, ESA, and the Hubble Heritage (STScI/AURA)-ESA/Hubble Collaboration. R. Chandar (University of Toledo) and J. Miller (University of Michigan). Public domain.

Back cover image: Vernon L. Smith at Acton University 2016. Credit: Mark Schmidbauer.

ACTONINSTITUTE

98 E. Fulton
Grand Rapids, Michigan 49503
616.454.3080
www.acton.org

Interior design: Judy Schafer
Cover design: Peter Ho

Printed in the United States of America

Contents

Foreword

"Historically, a recurrent theme in economics is that the values to which people respond are not confined to those one would expect based on the narrowly defined canons of rationality."[1] With these words delivered in his 2002 Nobel Prize lecture, the economist Vernon L. Smith directly challenged the common perception that economics assumes that human choices are essentially driven by selfishness. But he also indicated that the power of the human intellect might be in fact more expansive than much of modernity is willing to concede.

This message about the discipline famously labelled by Thomas Carlyle as "the dismal science" and about the everyday workings of free markets is one that more people need to hear. Careful reading of Smith's Nobel Prize lecture and his many other writings demonstrates just how much he has incorporated ideas about what makes people tick from other fields, ranging from philosophy to psychology, into his study of economics. The overall effect has been to help economics better reflect human reality rather than an artificial *homo economicus*. Such

---

[1] Vernon L. Smith, "Constructivist and Ecological Rationality in Economics," Nobel Prize Lecture, December 8, 2002, 503, https://www.nobelprize.org/nobel_prizes/economic-sciences/laureates/2002/smith-lecture.pdf.

work, however, is also indicative of Smith's lifelong willingness to engage sources of knowledge outside his discipline, some of which may surprise those unfamiliar with his work.

Among economists, Smith is known as one of the pioneers of the discipline of experimental economics. This involves laboratory-like experiments in which people are placed in a particular micro-economy in which they can engage in trade, but without knowing the conditions driving supply and demand in that micro-economy. Those running the experiments can thus test the validity of particular economic theories, thereby gaining greater knowledge of how economic exchanges actually work.

Over time, experimental economics has established the importance of what Smith and others call "economic institutions." Broadly speaking, there are the formal and informal rules (often called "protocols") that shape economic life in a given society. Smith's experiments have illustrated that economic institutions really *do* matter when it comes to shaping economic outcomes. Whether it is particular laws, regulations, customs, or property arrangements, any set of rules will affect (1) the information available to those in a given marketplace and (2) the incentives encouraging them to act in one way rather than another.

Smith's experiments have also provided considerable evidence that, as he wrote in a 1994 paper, "economic agents can achieve efficient outcomes which are not part of their intention." Many will recognize this as one of the central claims of *The Wealth of Nations*, the book written by Smith's famous namesake two and a half centuries ago. Interestingly, Adam Smith's argument was not one that Vernon Smith had been inclined to accept before beginning his experimental research. As the latter went on to say in his 1994 paper, "few outside of the Austrian and Chicago traditions believed it, circa 1956. Certainly I was not primed to believe it, having been raised by a socialist mother, and further handicapped (in this regard) by a Harvard education." Given, however, what his experiments revealed about what he called "the error in my thinking," Smith changed his mind. Truth was what mattered—not ego or preexisting ideological commitments.[2]

The Other Smith

This, however, was not the limit of Vernon Smith's engagement with the thought of Adam Smith and the Scottish Enlightenment more generally. Scottish Enlightenment thinkers such as Francis Hutcheson—a Presbyterian minister and the Chair of Moral Philosophy at the University of Glasgow (which Adam Smith himself later held)—were immensely influential upon the American founding, but also crucial to the development of modern market economies that, when permitted to do so, have liberated millions from poverty.

Though Vernon Smith is well versed in *The Wealth of Nations*, his writings emphasize the Scottish Enlightenment's attentiveness to the variety of human motivations that shape economic action. He has lamented more than once that most economists are unfamiliar with Adam Smith's other great work, *The Theory of Moral Sentiments* (1759), a text that Smith revised no less than six times and regarded as his most important book.

But what is especially important about the Scottish Enlightenment, from Vernon Smith's standpoint, is how it stimulated thought about the nature of reason. There is a place, Smith argues, for what is called "constructivist reason": the use of conscious deductive processes of human reason to establish social, political, and economic institutions. Drafting a constitu-

---

2   Vernon L. Smith, "Economics in a Laboratory," 1994, https://www.chapman.edu/research/institutes-and-centers/economic-science-institute/_files/AboutUs/Smith_EconomicsInLab.pdf#_blank.

tion is one example of this. Political order does not arise spontaneously. Human deliberation, choice, and action is involved.

Smith underscores, however, that the Scots also focused on another form of rationality: the reasonableness that is embodied and conveyed through time by *un-designed* habits, customs, and rules. We often do not fully understand the importance of such traditions, as Edmund Burke noted, until we dispose of them. A hallmark of Smith's work is his study of how such knowledge helps to mold political and economic outcomes.

Reason and Faith

One means by which such knowledge has been conveyed through time, Smith states, is religion. In a long footnote to his Nobel lecture, Smith stressed religion's role in shaping the morality needed for cohesive social behavior, "prominently represented by the great 'shalt not' prohibitions of the world's leading religions."[3] In his Nobel Prize banquet speech, Smith even singled out "the ancient Judeo Commandments" for providing the "foundations for cohesive social exchange."[4]

On one level, Smith was making an empirical claim. It is hard to imagine social and economic exchange being sustainable over the long term in the absence of the absolute prohibitions of practices such as, for example, theft and murder that were expressed in the Decalogue and vigorously reaffirmed by Jesus of Nazareth and Saint Paul. Widespread acceptance and internalization of such prohibitions lend a stability and certainty to legal devices such as contracts. Expecting legal systems to

---

[3] Smith, "Constructivist and Ecological Rationality in Economics," 509.

[4] Vernon L. Smith, "Banquet Speech," December 10, 2002, https://www.nobelprize.org/nobel_prizes/economic-sciences/laureates/2002/smith-speech.html.

be enough to discourage wrongful behavior is, from Smith's standpoint, somewhat naïve.

But Smith's appreciation of religion's importance as a source of knowledge also owes something to his Christian faith. This is not a topic about which Smith has often spoken at length, at least publicly. A major exception to that rule was the lecture published in this book, entitled "Faith and the Compatibility of Science and Religion."

Delivered at the Acton Institute's 2016 summer university, Smith's plenary lecture begins by describing how he had been raised in a Unitarian household before, during, and after the Great Depression. Eventually and very gradually, Smith states, he "was 'reborn' and baptized a Christian." This process, Smith specifies, was accelerated by reading the Lebanese mystical poet Kahlil Gibran (also singled out for praise in Smith's Nobel banquet speech), most notably Gibran's famous book of stories, *Jesus: The Son of Man*.[5]

Smith's lecture proceeds to present a clear-minded argument for the essential harmony between religious faith, science, and reason more generally. Drawing on the discoveries of twentieth-century physicists such as Albert Einstein and his colleague the Catholic priest Georges Lemaître (the first to propose the theory of the expansion of the universe as well as the Big Bang theory), Smith argues that the basic claims of materialist philosophy have been disproved by reason and scientific inquiry. He also highlights similarities between (1) the insights attained via modern physics and (2) the language and logic deployed in

---

5   Smith, "Faith and the Compatibility of Science and Religion," 2. Gibran is also cited at the beginning of the introduction to one of Smith's most widely read books, *Rationality in Economics: Constructivist and Ecological Forms*, which was dedicated to his wife, Candace Cavanah Smith, who was also present for the lecture.

the Hebrew and Christian Scriptures to describe God as First Cause and the origin of Creation.

Certainly, Smith notes, Einstein was right to claim that the theories designed by humans are important tools for comprehending reality. Yet before there is theory, Smith adds, there is thought and reason, a logical sequence that, he says, finds its parallel in the opening verse of the gospel of John: "In the beginning was the Word [*Logos*], and the Word was with God, and the Word was God" (1:1 KJV).

Put another way, human reason cannot emerge from unreason. Ultimately it comes from and reflects the light of the *Logos* himself. We can be confident, Smith concluded, that life is no accident. "We Christians," he said, "believe it was a loving act of our God and our Savior—a faith that is compatible with the engineering discoveries we call science."[6] For that same loving God is also Divine Reason, from which all truth proceeds, and who has ordered our minds so that we can, dimly, understand much of that truth through natural reason—a natural reason that itself provides access to knowledge of this God, which is supplemented by Divine Revelation.

And Economics?

What, then, does this mean for economics? These themes are addressed in the materials supplementing Smith's Acton University lecture. In two interviews of Smith (the first conducted by me and the second by Victor Claar), he addresses some common misunderstandings of economics that are often articulated by people of faith. He illustrates, for instance, how careful we should be before we associate greed with what Adam Smith describes as "self-interest" in his *Wealth of Nations*.

---

6   Smith, "Faith and the Compatibility of Science and Religion," 19.

By most accounts, Adam Smith was not a Christian (though the vast majority of his contemporaries in the Scottish Enlightenment certainly were) and was most likely a Deist. But his conception of self-interest, says Vernon Smith, must be unpacked and placed in the context of what Adam Smith wrote about other-regarding behavior in both *The Wealth of Nations* and his *Theory of Moral Sentiments*. This soon makes one realize that Adam Smith was much more attentive to the complex range of intentions and motivations that underlie human choice and human action than he is often assumed to have been.

Philosophers are often skilled at explicating these underlying causes. But so too are the Scriptures. They give us insights into the mind of the Creator that reason could never attain by itself. Vernon Smith views the enterprise of economic science as part of that great exploration by man's reason into the workings of the human mind, as we look for "evidence of things not seen," Smith says, citing the letter to the Hebrews (11:1 KJV). As Lenore Ealy writes in her commentary on Smith's paper, Smith regards "the quest for understanding" to be "the shared fount of faith and science." In that sense, she argues that Smith's work should stimulate "more economists" to reflect "on their own methodologies, the predominant liturgies of the modern economics priesthood, and the meaning of it all."[7]

After a lifetime of achievement in economics, Vernon Smith reminds us that reason and Christian faith should never be seen as necessary opponents. In different but compatible and interrelated ways, both are essentially concerned with knowing the truth, the pursuit of the fullness of which, the gospel of John tells us, is what sets us free (8:32).

Samuel Gregg
Director of Research
Acton Institute

---

[7] Lenore T. Ealy, "Comment," 21, 35.

Faith and the Compatibility of Science and Religion*

Vernon L. Smith

I am especially grateful that Acton has given me this opportunity to speak on faith—faith as I see it manifest in scientific and religious experience from ancient to modern times. As you can imagine, it is not a topic that my fellow economists would have invited me to consider. I do not pretend to speak from any scholarly expertise, but merely as an individual searching for personal answers to ancient human questions. Each of us has to seek our own answers while learning from the experiences of others, guided by our spiritual understanding.

Truth seeking—through love—was a powerful Christian commitment long before it became the centerpiece of the scientific enterprise.

What is faith and how might it be relevant to both science and religion? The answer I will use is a New Testament definition that also applies to science. Hebrews 11:1: "Now faith is

---

* This lecture was delivered on June 16, 2016, at the Acton Institute's annual conference, Acton University, in Grand Rapids, Michigan. Portions of this lecture previously appeared in Vernon L. Smith, *Discovery—A Memoir* (Bloomington, IN: AuthorHouse, 2008), 361–65; and in Smith, "Faith, Science and Religion," in *Eminent Economists II—Their Life and Work Philosophies*, ed. Michael Szenberg and Lall B. Ramratten (New York: Cambridge University Press, 2014), 369–88.

the substance of things hoped for, the evidence of things not seen" (KJV). The meaning expressed here applies just as fundamentally to science as to religion; both are concerned with the invisible realities of truth.

My early exposure to religion in the 1930s was defined by the prevailing materialistic-agnostic interpretation of science at the time. My mother and her father had been attracted to Unitarianism before I was born. Unitarians sought to re-craft their religious beliefs to embody the perspectives of science. But this was the fashionable face of reason that was always tempered and qualified by an inner, private experience emanating from deeper secular and Judaic-Christian sources of poetic inspiration that left its mark upon me. Ultimately, I was "reborn" and baptized a Christian. My ever so grateful and gradual conversion process probably was accelerated by Kahlil Gibran, the Lebanese poet, when I read his *Jesus: The Son of Man*. It was the right blend of sacred, secular, and mystical writings that became ever more meaningful to me as I reread it.

Although materialism is alive and well in the rhetoric of scientists and intellectuals today, the truth-seeking processes of science have made it obsolete. Materialism is dead, not God; if God was thought dead for a while he has been resurrected. There is no conflict between science and religion; by conventional materialist standards, the two are equally spooky.

The basic materialist faith was nurtured by the expectation that physical science would enable us to determine the ultimate reductionist building blocks of matter. In that discovery we would come to understand our universe at a depth that would subvert and replace any need for appealing to spiritual or mystical entities to comprehend human existence. Personally, this expectation was implicit in my naïve childhood belief that everything would become knowable to me once I became an adult. I had yet to learn that along with the answer to any question came a host of deeper questions contained in the answer.

This unending shells-within-shells characteristic of our search for understanding is revealed in every generation by the child who forces you to the outer limits of knowledge by asking "Why?" three times in sequence followed by your attempts to answer. This questioning and probing to find deeper levels of comprehension, to explain the explanation, is unique to neither science nor religion; it is a manifestation of human ignorance, curiosity, and inquiry, the hunger to know. Hence, the wisdom of the directive to become as little children (see Matt. 18:3).

The materialist conception of the universe started to unravel with two of Einstein's four famous papers published in 1905, one on the special theory of relativity,[1] the other on the photoelectric effect.[2] One of the implications of the first was the equivalence of energy and matter, leading to a revolutionary new understanding of physics that had practical applications in nuclear energy. It was followed in 1916 by his general theory of relativity, which reinterpreted our concept of gravity, space, and time, and later formed the basis for the cosmology of an expanding universe starting with the Big Bang of creation.

Today, these relativistic extensions of Newtonian physics are seen as straightforward modifications of classical physics and live entirely embraced within the substance of the classical paradigm. At their time these extensions were counterintuitive, because our intuition was so bound and distorted by the sense that space and time existed as independent experiences. Neither the imagination nor its mathematical products, however, were constrained by human sense experience or the instruments of the day. And this led to new theorems, experiments, and instrumental techniques that greatly expanded human comprehension.

Einstein's second 1905 paper established that energy came in discrete packets that were governed by a strange form of

---

[1] *Annalen der Physik* 17 (1905): 891–921.

[2] *Annalen der Physik* 17 (1905): 132–48.

probabilistic uncertainty in nature; this is the topic cited when he won the Nobel Prize in 1921 and jump-started the field of quantum mechanics. As Einstein put it, with characteristic intuitive simplicity in 1905, "When a ray of light is spreading from a point, the energy is not distributed continuously over ever-increasing spaces, but consists of a finite number of energy quanta that are localized in points in space, move without dividing, and can be absorbed or generated only as a whole."[3]

The new breakthrough, quantum physics, would later be discovered to imply a "spooky action at a distance" that Einstein could never accept, although it defined a new observational reality that eventually received experimental support many times over. Others would not be restrained by the intuitive unreality of the new physics and would simply follow the mathematics and the new experiments into a quantitative world that was mystical by all previous standards.

Indeed Einstein's early influence on others was substantial, and the backstory of his fundamental contributions has been carefully articulated by A. D. Stone.[4] Thus, Stone's chapter 25, "Quantum Dice," changes the common image of Einstein as having been swept aside by the tide of events in quantum theory. It was Einstein that had the key insight in 1925 that interchanging the role of two identical particles did not constitute a distinct state of matter. If two particles each have two states, there are not four distinguishable states, but three: like "quantum" coins, with states TT, HH, and HT-TH-oneness. And generally the off-diagonal state pairs (i, j) are not distin-

---

[3] Albert Einstein, "On a Heuristic Point of View Concerning the Production and Transformation of Light," in *The Collected Papers of Albert Einstein*, vol. 2, *The Swiss Years: Writings, 1900–1909*, trans. Anna Beck (Princeton, NJ: Princeton University Press, 1989), 87.

[4] A. Douglas Stone, *Einstein and the Quantum: The Quest of the Valiant Swabian* (Princeton, NJ: Princeton University Press, 2013).

guishable. Particle states bunch together in nature, explaining why matter is matter. It underpins Bose-Einstein condensates, accounting for phenomena such as super-liquefaction and super-conductivity that connect our experience with the reality of this mysterious calculus of quantum probability.

In his correspondence with Einstein, the young Schrödinger thought Einstein had made a mistake calculating the probabilities, but Einstein replied that although Schrödinger's concerns were justified (by standard classical probability theory), his paper did not have a calculation error, and he states the 2×2, three-distinct-state example. Schrödinger got it. Einstein's letter was the key! And Schrödinger was led to his brilliant wave-particle equations![5]

A new mystery arrived with Hubble's 1929 discovery that the stars and galaxies of the universe are expanding in all directions at velocities that increase in proportion to their distance from us. The implication was that our space-time universe had a single region of origin. The idea had been proposed by Lemaître, the Belgian cosmologist and Catholic priest, in the year of my birth, 1927. In 1949 the British astronomer Fred Hoyle dubbed it appropriately, "the Big Bang." And that was the label that stuck. For perhaps thirty years scientists, including Hoyle, were very resistant to the idea that all matter and energy in the universe must have once emanated from a particular historical region in space-time. Mathematicians called it a "singularity," massive compared with the singularities sprinkled in all directions throughout the universe like Swiss cheese, and associated with local imploded stars, or black holes.

Why this resistance? I think it emanates from the Newtonian idea that the universe had always existed, which seemed psychologically more comforting and natural—no beginning, no end. If there was a beginning, then science—the search for truth

---

[5]   Stone, *Einstein and the Quantum*, 240.

in physical phenomena—had to face up to the psychologically overwhelming fact that before the beginning there was nothing: no matter, no energy, no space, no time, just a monstrously pervasive nothing! (I use *nothing* here in the sense of classical physics, not in the sense of quantum physics.) But if the universe had always existed, then it seemed that there was room aplenty for Einstein's impersonal God, the deism of natural rules, order, and beauty. How would you imagine and how do you model the nothing that became something?

Our ancestors had understood their world in terms of Genesis 1:2. Before creation there was a formless void and darkness covered the face of the deep. While in our day, the time of the Big Bang, we have come to understand our world, technically, as originating at a massive singularity for which the equations that chart everything from stars and energy to planets have no finite solution.

The ancient question of human existence, "Why is there something rather than nothing?" could be avoided if this something that we observe everywhere was thought to have always existed—in direct contradiction to Genesis and to Hebrews 11:3, where it is stated that "by faith we understand that the universe was ordered by the word of God, so that what is visible came into being through the invisible" (NABRE). But the new question for science, implicit in the Big Bang theory, "Why was there nothing that became something?" seemed to deepen the state of our ignorance and mystery. This is because the mystery of origins is beyond any conceivable science and beyond the traditional apparatus of hypothesis testing. Creation—that is, the beginning—could be located in the backward trajectory of history, and in the limiting state of equations that have again and again proved to have enormous experimental and astrophysical predictive power when they were used to locate events in our observable world of space-time, energy, and matter.

These developments, and those in quantum physics, can only be described as embarrassing for classical materialism. That the materialist rhetoric is little changed tells you how deep its belief system penetrated. This is delightfully illustrated in an interview of Richard Dawkins, my favorite atheist (because he is supremely self-confident), who was asked, "Have you ever felt the presence of what they call the Divine, whether it was being moved by music, or some sort of church?" The great expert's reply was, "Yes," but that he "wouldn't wish to use the word 'divine' because it is so easily misunderstood." Dawkins continued,

> When I think of the wonder I feel about the physical universe, yes, I feel that. I wouldn't call it 'divine.' But something like when I listen to Schubert or look at a great cathedral or look at the Grand Canyon, I do get a feeling which is probably akin to what religious people feel when they experience what they call a mystical experience. I don't think there's anything supernatural about it. I think it's all going on in my material brain. But I wouldn't wish to be upstaged by a religious person when it comes to my ability to feel an emotional response to something like a beautiful piece of music or a beautiful object.[6]

So please tell us, Richard, just what is this "material brain" that makes that wondrous experience so easy for you to understand, that erases any need to appeal to the supernatural, and that is scientific? The child in Richard Dawkins should ask "Why?" one more time. Science cannot find anything in the brain's ultimate constituents except energy that is both particle and wavelike and causes blips on our classical instruments.

---

[6] Richard Dawkins, "Richard Dawkins: I'm not like Christopher Hitchens!," interview by Daniel D'Addario, *Salon*, September 29, 2013, https://www.salon.com/2013/09/29/richard_dawkins_im _not_like_christopher_hitchens/.

Stephen Hawking, in *A Briefer History of Time*, allows that physics has put a new twist on origins. The Big Bang began in an initial state that cannot be represented by Einstein's general theory of gravity. Hawking asks how, if God chose the laws of nature, he managed to choose the initial state. Quantum theory, he says, offers a remedy, as it allows space-time to be finite but with no boundary singularities, as on the surface of a billiard ball or doughnut, except with a few more dimensions that we cannot translate into experience.[7] (In that last sentence I initially had used the word *intuition* instead of *experience*. Then I realized that intuition itself cannot be accounted for inside the box of our world experience and must have higher dimensional representations, access to which cannot be credibly proven.)

What became the Standard Model triumphed with the discovery of the Higgs boson particle and reignited the puzzle of why the fundamental constants, the velocity of light or the charge on the electron, have the values we observe. If they did not have the particular values they do, we would not be here to be puzzled. What physicists call the anthropic puzzle, others call God. Even we humans can imagine a more general model that yields these constants as predicted observations rather than key crutches in our empirical approximations used to account for the world of experience. Think of the universe as one of a great many alternatives with these so-called constants as the particular realizations of variables that enable our presence.

But what is this thing we call experience? Beyond science is a personal experience shared by the ancients and all humans today, a sense of the awe and mystery of existence. For me this experience must count as an observation even if it is considered incommensurate with our rhetorical vision of the objective tests

---

[7] Stephen Hawking, *A Briefer History of Time* (New York: Bantam, 2005), 102–3.

of science. That power to inspire awe is magically expressed in Carruth's moving lines,

> Like tides on a crescent sea-beach,
>   When the moon is new and thin,
> Into our hearts high yearnings
>   Come welling and surging in:
> Come from the mystic ocean
>   Whose rim no foot has trod,—
> Some of us call it Longing,
>   And others call it God.[8]

Materialism ignores any references to experiences of awe and mystery as evidence of the nonmaterial. Dawkins, and perhaps most scientists, rule out such experiences as evidence that stretches beyond the scientific horizon. Since they do not count as observations, we do not have to explain or pursue an understanding of them, much as we did not have to account for a beginning if the universe had always existed. What is not an observation does not enter our world view. Kahlil Gibran may have had such dismissals at heart in his book *The Madman*, where he writes,

> We heard a voice crying, "This is the sea. This is the deep sea. This is the vast and mighty sea." And when we reached the voice it was a man whose back was turned to the sea, and at his ear he held a shell, listening to its murmur. And my soul said, "Let us pass on. He is the realist, who turns his back on the whole he cannot grasp, and busies himself with a fragment."[9]

---

[8] William Herbert Carruth, "Each in His Own Tongue," in *Each in His Own Tongue and Other Poems* (New York: Putnam, 1908), 2–3.

[9] Kahlil Gibran, *The Madman: His Parables and Poems* (New York: Alfred A. Knopf, 1918), 54–55.

Science has chosen to become more and more deeply informed on a fragment of the total human experience, with most scientists believing that the fragment constitutes the whole, and clinging to it. The words "material brain" constitute part of that whole, however empty. The belief is unshakable when it is coupled with the belief that contrary experiences do not count as observations. What is paradoxical is that the success of science has always depended crucially on the emergence of scientists with an open mind to phenomena. Yet areas seen as contaminated by belief error in the past are not fit for openness. These areas include not only religious and philosophical explorations, but physical science in the past, as when the earth was believed to be the center of the universe.

Returning to Einstein, what eventually spooked him about quantum theory was illustrated by the discovery that two quantum particles could interact instantaneously no matter where they were separately located in our universe of classical instrumental experience. In experiments in Switzerland, such particles are studied at a separation of 18 kilometers![10] Thus, if one particle is perturbed, there is an instantaneous synchronous effect on the other. This seemed to violate special relativity by allowing physics to embrace speeds greater than that of light. The best verbal description that could be mustered was the concept that two such particles are "entangled"—the term introduced by Schrödinger in 1935—a phenomenon subsequently found over and over to be consistent with indirect experimental observations. The common origin of the particles—a kind of twinning—binds them in a relationship that defies the logic

---

[10] Daniel Salart et al., "Testing the Speed of 'Spooky Action at a Distance,'" *Nature* 454, no. 7206 (August 14, 2008): 861–64, doi:10.1038/nature07121; cf. Terence G. Rudolph, "The Speed of Instantly," *Nature* 454, no. 7206 (August 14, 2008): 831–32, doi:10.1038/454831a.

and intuition of Einstein's new classical physics. But let me emphasize that all perception, and all scientific observations, are indirect, and are therefore necessarily the "evidence of things not seen," as in Hebrews 11:1.

Even if quantum theory is "incomplete" and due for improvement, scientists now have faith that quantum-spooky interconnectedness will be retained. Indeed, what does it mean to say that two entangled particles are subject to "simultaneous" effects? It means that the time required by any postulated signal passing between the two particles is below the detection limit of the instruments. What the Swiss experiments show is that any supposed signal passing between the entangled particles must be traveling at least ten thousand times the speed of light! An implication is that if they are connected via a higher dimensional space, no shadow is cast in our space-time world of experience, at least not that we know how to detect with existing knowledge and instruments.

I have used the phrase "objective tests of science," which carries the ring of "reality," but this is a rhetorical distraction. "Reality," when penetrated by new instrumental probes, is never what it seems in our experience of the world, and no one was a greater champion of this principle than Einstein. For example, he used the term "ponderable matter" in contrasting elements of classical physics with his new space-time physics. His general relativity theory created an interpretation of space—a mathematical equivalence—that curved back on itself in a four-dimensional space-time continuum.

Einstein had long known that the theory had to show that gravity and acceleration were indistinguishable. A simple mental experiment gave him the proof, the inner conviction, the substance of things hoped for. Imagine that you are in a sealed chamber within a rocket ship, unable to observe anything outside of it. You feel and can measure your weight or force against the floor. There is no experiment that you can perform that can reveal whether you are accelerating under propulsion in empty outer space or in an orbit under the influence of gravity in the proximity of a star or a planet. In either case a dropped object falls to the floor. So gravity and acceleration have to be equivalent, and that led Einstein to eventually develop the mathematics of that.

Truth must come packaged in the form of experience. Experience can be imagined, based on mental constructs available from internal mental information, or it can be a construct built from external stimuli received through our senses. If your mind cannot tell the difference between internal and external signals you may be afflicted with schizophrenia, but otherwise be entirely "normal." (As Lily Tomlin once said, "Why is it that when we talk to God we're said to be praying, but when God talks to us we're schizophrenic?")

Incredibly, as Einstein and others would show, the space curvature of general relativity allows for the theoretical possibility of "wormholes" through which various points in space are accessibly connected by shortcuts that, if traversable, do not violate special relativity but simply bypass it. In particular, gravity is not instantaneous, but is mediated by a finite signal that, through the warping of space-time, travels only at the speed of light. Keep in mind that we are talking of theory, some implications of which have survived experimental tests, at least where observations could be brought to bear on certain of its predictions, beginning with the eclipse experiments of Eddington in 1919. The wormhole solution has remained speculative without observational support, and its main influence has been on science fiction. The equations of the theory exist whatever our attempts to interpret them. A recent hot topic in theory seeks to link wormhole relativity with quantum entanglement and connects to "multiverse" (parallel universes) interpretations. Some call it physics; others call it God.[11]

What is mind-boggling—Feynman said that nobody understands quantum mechanics—is that uncertainty, unpredictability, is built into the micro foundations that support all that we experience. Physics is based on modeling relationships, changes in the position and momentum of a mass. The state of a billiard ball is entirely determined when we measure its position on the table and its momentum—mass times velocity—where speed can be determined by a radar gun. Our sense experience, leveraged with instruments, is that of a determinate position and momentum for the ball. But at the micro level of measurement, applied originally by Heisenberg to a particle, there is an unresolvable uncertainty that was not thought to be shared by the billiard ball example. As Heisenberg proved, there are natural uncertainty limits on our ability to independently measure the position and momentum of a particle. At the micro measurement level the more certainly we determine a particle's position, the less certainly we determine its momentum. The product of these uncertainties (probabilities) is constrained numerically by a value proportional to a universal constant due to Max Planck. (The product cannot be smaller than $h/4\pi$, where h is Planck's constant.) This is because at the instant the particle's position is known the photon (radar gun-like) measurement process discontinuously jumps the level of the particle's momentum. Hence, at the instant that the position is known the particle's momentum can be known only up to the level corresponding to that discontinuous jump.

So what? Isn't this only at the particle level expressed by wave equations? Not quite. Any mass can be represented by an

---

[11] Charles Q. Choi, "Spooky Physics Phenomenon May Link Universe's Wormholes," *Live Science*, December 3, 2013, http://www.livescience.com/41639-quantum-entanglement-linkswormholes.html.

equivalent wave function. The propagation of that billiard ball has an equivalent wave energy description. Measuring its position and momentum encounters exactly the same uncertainty as a particle *at the Planck level of smallness*. We are talking about what happens when we examine things at very micro levels, whatever the thing might be. The principle is not altered by our single-minded insistence on ignoring small effects at billiard ball macro levels. Think of there being a layer of quantum active support everywhere, underlying all that we experience and perceive in the world, and that reality is beset with quantum unpredictability. This is the way that Nature—others call it God—works. In principle any classical body can exist in two quantum states (or a superposition) at the same time. There is no boundary separating quantum from classical phenomena into two distinct and independent realities.

The world of our sense experiences is coarse enough that we are far, far above the Planck layer of smallness; simultaneously our world involves speeds that are tiny with respect to the velocity of light. The latter property allows us to live blithely unaware that with increased speed masses grow heavier, clocks run slower, measuring rods shrink, space and time is one—space-time. Einstein, spooked by the implications for physics of Planck smallness, felt at home from the start with relativity, which disturbed other physicists for decades. Einstein won the relativity battles with others, but not the quantum battle with himself. And only recently it was reported that new experiments "push quantum superposition into a new macroscopic regime, demonstrating that quantum superposition remains possible at the distances and timescales of everyday life."[12]

---

[12] T. Kovachy et al., "Quantum Superposition at the Half-Metre Scale," *Nature* 528, no. 7583 (December 24, 2015): 530, doi:10.1038/nature16155.

Contemporary theorists have learned to take quantum incredibility at equation, if not face, value. In less than a hundred years after the special theory and the photoelectric effect, we encountered engineering miracles such as atomic energy, all-electronic devices, and lasers. The field of chemistry, and therefore biology, is rooted and nurtured in that pervasive layer modeled by quantum theory. So we should not shoot from the hip in rejecting entangled objects and teleportation as the stuff only of fantasy or science fiction. Indeed, teleportation in the sense of information transfer has been achieved in atoms and molecules. At quantum levels, if you have copied all the information in an object, you have teleported that object. These fairy tale–like stories are now serious physics within the framework of contemporary science; some have yet to lead anywhere tangible, others have led to breakthrough observations and devices.

The point I want to emphasize is that science is about physical and biological mechanisms, about discovering how things work, about engineering, about theories that describe and can predict observations that we experience entirely through our senses or their extension through instruments. It is the instruments of science that supply us with the indirect evidence of things not seen. It is like Plato's allegory of the cave, in which reality can only be experienced as shadows on a cave wall. An experimental physicist says that he measures the "spin" of an electron, but in actuality he records certain effects on a screen and uses the theory (his faith) to calculate its meaning as a measurement. In 1932 Carl Anderson discovered the positron, but actually he photographed a high energy trace in a cloud chamber, surrounded by an electromagnet. From the theory he could infer from the curvature of the trace that it was a particle with a positive charge. Science keeps getting better, in this instrumental task, on a scale beyond anything that could be believed possible in 1905, let alone at the beginning of the Christian era.

In science we observe nothing directly; only indirectly through instruments that record the secondary effects implied by conceptual models of things—particles, waves, energy—whose postulated existence is not violated by these indirect observations. But you cannot derive the existence of those objects and the richness of the theory from the sparse indirect effects and the measurements we record—theory is resolutely underdetermined by observation. You can only do the reverse: deduce from those constructed things and model their implications for what we can expect to observe.

The constructs come from mysterious flights of the imagination, from scientific intuition buttressed by mathematics. That undergirding structure, the theory, the hope that drives imagination, are what you accept on faith. The believability of that faith is reinforced by the occasional tests that one is lucky and ingenious enough to perform, until that faith is disturbed by contrary observations, or a more comprehensive construct, to account for new shadows on the cave wall of our experience.

Hence, what is inescapable is the dependence of science on faith. The conceptual and theoretical constructs of science constitute the substance of things hoped for and observational support depends on instruments that record the evidence of things not seen. As Einstein once said, "It is the theory which decides what can be observed."[13] But I must add that prior to theory there is what we call "thinking"—a systematic form of consciousness deeply driven by the unconscious that enables understanding and experimental predictions. The parallel is expressed in John 1:1, "In the beginning was the Word, and the Word was with God, and the Word was God" (KJV). For humans, all beginnings are in thought or reason. And in the reductionist search

---

[13] As recounted by Werner Heisenberg, "Tradition in Science," in *Encounters with Einstein: And Other Essays on People, Places, and Particles* (Princeton, NJ: Princeton University Press, 1983), 10.

for reality, science can only identify mind, first in things hoped for, then in the assurance of unseen evidence.

This unseen reality of theory brings an operating understanding of how our world works, and enables us to accomplish engineering miracles by trial, error, tinkering, and adjustment. What person living one hundred years ago could have even imagined the material marvels that would exist routinely today?

Science, however, cannot identify, nor can it disprove, purpose. Some prominent scientists and philosophers have claimed—somewhat intemperately, it seems—that science shows that there is no purpose in the universe. The denial of purpose goes hand in hand with the denial that a sense of mystery is an admissible observation. But failing to find something does not allow one to conclude therefore that it does not exist. Scientists embrace this proposition wholeheartedly in space explorations, in the search for extraterrestrial intelligence (SETI); also in various Mars probes, a hot research topic is whether there is evidence of life in some simple cellular form. Failing to find any smoking-gun evidence for life has not deterred continuance of the search, nor has it suppressed belief that life can be generated spontaneously from unfathomable physical processes. Scientists therefore accept that failing to find evidence of extraterrestrial life or intelligence does not prove their nonexistence.

In religious matters, however, scientists tend to identify the lack of observable evidence for purpose as supporting the proposition that there is no purpose—a contradiction with the assertion that lack of evidence of extraterrestrial life does not mean that it does not exist. Religions everywhere have sought to comprehend a universal, purposeful human experience: a longing born of high yearnings that come welling and surging in, that are indeed believed to come from a mystic ocean on whose rim no foot has trod.

The ancients confounded their mystical experience and religious faith with explanations of everyday events. Science has invaded that everyday world of explanation and created marvels out of the new understanding of how things work. Ancient peoples believed that the formation and movement of clouds were governed by divine forces. Science demonstrates that clouds are a precipitate of water vapor under specified conditions of temperature, pressure, and saturation.

But knowing the engineering properties of a cloud does not make it any less mysterious or less "divine." The mystery is simply pushed to a more fundamental level. The technological success of science cannot be construed as supporting the opinions of scientists that concern matters beyond current science. Our accelerating ability to utilize the workings of complex systems creates an illusion of comprehension, of control, even understanding, but it leaves in place the gap between engineering and purpose. That illusion—Dawkins calls it his "material brain"—is what maintains a wedge between science and religion. The scope of the engineering is expanded, deepening the mystery of meaning. Better, deeper, and ever more knowledge of how—consistent with but commonly not specifically predicted by theory—does not answer why.

Moreover, quantum theory models the ultimate phenomena that are simultaneously beyond our capacity to experience in space-time, and from which that space-time world has emerged. Twentieth century science, mirrorlike, brought the search for reality face to face with the mysticism that it rejected. Science now rejects the hypothesis that there exists a boundary separating the classical physics of our experience from the quantum world of wave energy that collapses into "particle traces" when we measure them.

In closing I want to reemphasize that science has brought us full circle. Our sense of mystery is an observation consistent with the religious faith of our fathers. Christian theology is the counterpart of theory in science. Our experience of the Spirit is our evidence. Both scientific and religious understanding are advanced by being able to imagine and experience more than we can prove or verify.

And what a glorious experience to be alive. Scientists have said it was an accident, without purpose. We Christians believe it was a loving act of our God and our Savior—a faith that is compatible with the engineering discoveries we call science.

Thank you, ladies and gentlemen. And may peace be with you.

Comment on Vernon Smith's 'Faith and the Compatibility of Science and Religion'

Lenore T. Ealy[*]

I am honored to be invited to comment on Vernon Smith's address "Faith and the Compatibility of Science and Religion." I heard Professor Smith deliver this address at Acton University in 2016 and admired then, as I do now, his willingness to share his journey in reconciling his faith with his scientific commitments and practice. While there are many scientists who manage successfully to harmonize personal faith with their scholarly pursuits despite the present climate in our secular universities, few are called upon to make public profession. As Smith notes in thanking the Acton Institute for the invitation to speak on the topic, "it is not a topic that my fellow economists would have invited me to consider."[1]

At the core of Smith's profession is the observation that the quest for understanding is the shared fount of faith and science. "This questioning and probing to find deeper levels of comprehension, to explain the explanation," he writes, "is

---

[*]   Lenore T. Ealy is President of The Philanthropic Enterprise, a not-for-profit research institute that seeks to strengthen our understanding of how philanthropy and voluntary social cooperation promote human flourishing. She holds a Ph.D. in the history of moral and political thought from Johns Hopkins University.
[1]   Smith, "Faith and the Compatibility of Science and Religion," 1.

unique to neither science nor religion; it is a manifestation of human ignorance, curiosity, and inquiry, the hunger to know." The tension between science and religion, Smith tells us, is largely attributable to the hold that materialism—the "expectation that physical science would enable us to determine the ultimate reductionist building blocks of matter"—acquired among scientists prior to the relativistic and quantum revolution in physics.[2] Walking us deftly through the discoveries of physicists in the last century, beginning with Einstein's four published papers in 1905, Smith explains how the classical materialist framework began to unravel.

This is not easy going; Smith acquaints us here with the challenges of understanding the space-time continuum, the observation that matter is both particle and wave, the introduction of the new cosmology of the Big Bang, and the thorny concepts of entanglement. Even Einstein, who could imagine riding on a light beam, was reluctant to accept the proposition of quantum mechanics that two quantum particles located at vast distances in the universe can interact instantaneously. Smith, however, drives straight to the heart of the matter and embraces the implication that "spooky action at a distance" implied by theories of entanglement has made materialism obsolete while resurrecting God. For Smith, modern physics opened a way to reconcile the tensions between science and religion, since both are now concerned "with the invisible realities of truth."[3] If faith is the substance of things hoped for but not seen, particle physics now points to a new reality that is the proper object of both science and faith.

Smith's point is methodological and epistemological; he observes that the belief that science rests on "objective tests" has served more rhetorical distraction than pointer to reality.

---

[2] Smith, "Faith and the Compatibility of Science and Religion," 2.

[3] Smith, "Faith and the Compatibility of Science and Religion," 2.

"Reality," Smith writes, "is never what it seems in our experience of the world."

> In science we observe nothing directly; only indirectly through instruments that record the secondary effects implied by conceptual models of things—particles, waves, energy—whose postulated existence is not violated by these indirect observations. But you cannot derive the existence of those objects and the richness of the theory from the sparse indirect effects and the measurements we record—theory is resolutely underdetermined by observation. You can only do the reverse: deduce from those constructed things and models their implications for what we can expect to observe.[4]

As we delve farther into the micro levels of measurement, we experience reality, as in Plato's allegory, only "as shadows on a cave wall." Exploring the quantum level of reality requires the development of constructs that "come from mysterious flights of the imagination, from scientific intuition buttressed by mathematics." Moreover, we confront greater uncertainty (as Heisenberg taught us), and what we know becomes less reliant on observation and more dependent upon probabilities and computational mathematics. Contemporary theorists now accept, despite their inability to directly perceive it, that "reality is beset with quantum unpredictability." "This," Smith concludes, "is the way that Nature—others call it God—works."[5]

The upshot of all this is that "fairy tale–like stories are now serious physics" or, in other words, that scientific inquiry depends as much upon faith in things hoped for and not yet seen as does religious experience. Whereas science employs conceptual models and instruments, religious faith turns on another

---

4   Smith, "Faith and the Compatibility of Science and Religion," 16.
5   Smith, "Faith and the Compatibility of Science and Religion," 15, 16, 14.

observable category of human experience, what Smith describes as "a sense of the awe and mystery of existence."[6] Materialists fumble about trying to explain human behavior in terms of material structures and processes in the brain, focusing only on a fragment of human experience. Deaf to the roar of the ocean because they are straining to hear the whisper from the shell (Smith invokes the verses of Kahlil Gibran to make his point here[7]), materialists have "intemperately" claimed that science shows that there is no purpose in the universe. Smith will have none of this. "The technological success of science," he insists, "cannot be construed as supporting the opinions of scientists that concern matters beyond current science. Our accelerating ability to utilize the workings of complex systems creates an illusion of comprehension, of control, even understanding, but it leaves in place the gap between engineering and purpose."[8]

Science can disprove neither the existence of a purposeful divinity nor our experience of the things of the Spirit. Moreover, the deeper science takes us into understanding the nature of things the more we come full circle to confront mysteries the answers to which require imaginative leaps of faith.

* * *

---

[6] Smith, "Faith and the Compatibility of Science and Religion," 15, 8.

[7] There is striking similarity here to the observation of C. S. Lewis in his essay "The Weight of Glory," where he writes, "It would seem that Our Lord finds our desires not too strong, but too weak. We are half-hearted creatures, fooling about with drink and sex and ambition when infinite joy is offered us, like an ignorant child who wants to go on making mud pies in a slum because he cannot imagine what is meant by the offer of a holiday at the sea. We are far too easily pleased" (*The Weight of Glory and Other Addresses* [1949; New York: HarperOne, 2001], 26).

[8] Smith, "Faith and the Compatibility of Science and Religion," 17, 18.

Smith's account of the unraveling of materialism by modern physics is inviting and interesting, so far as it goes to explain how one of the most accomplished scholars of our time reconciles faith and science. Nevertheless, Smith's offering leaves me wishing that he had ventured a little farther, both to address some of the persistent redoubts of materialism today and to introduce the story of how he brings his faith to bear (if he does) in his own practices as an experimental economist. The latter explication is especially desirable because of the extent to which Smith's work is entwined with the emerging fields of evolutionary psychology and neuroeconomics, which at face value can often appear to rely upon the old reductionist premise that explanations for the actions of the human mind may best be found in material structures and functions.[9]

In his introduction to the English translation of F. A. Lange's *The History of Materialism*, the philosopher and Nobel Laureate (literature) Bertrand Russell acknowledged that modern physics (much as Smith affirms) has challenged the assumptions of hard (metaphysical) materialism:

---

[9]   Neuroeconomist Paul Zak asserts, for instance, that "trust is chemical." While Zak's recommendations for enhancing trust in the workplace focus on how managers' behaviors can elicit physiological oxytocin-based trust responses among employees, it is not a far leap to imagine the Brave New Worlds that might take shape as less scrupulous managers armed with chemical recipes for trust and sociality (or compliance or aggression or some other desired human behavior) might simply administer a chemical cocktail to attain these ends. Such "hacking" of human behavior, even more so perhaps than the desire to implement "nudging" through public policy design, poses ethical questions that should not be ignored by those whose moral anthropology embraces the freedom and dignity of the human person. See Zak, "The Neuroscience of Trust," *People and Strategy* 37, no. 1 (2014): 14–17, http://www.neuroeconomicstudies.org/images/stories/documents/37.2_Research_corner_Round_3.compressed.pdf.

> The theory of relativity, by merging time into space-time, has damaged the traditional notion of substance more than all the arguments of philosophers. Matter, for common-sense, is something which persists in time and moves in space. But for modern relativity-physics this view is no longer tenable. A piece of matter has become, not a persistent thing with varying states, but a system of inter-related events. The old solidity is gone, and with it the characteristics that, to the materialist, made matter seem more real than fleeting thoughts. Nothing is permanent, nothing endures, the prejudice that the real is the persistent must be abandoned.[10]

Russell further remarked, however, that the field of psychology, despite the quantum turn in physics, has persistently maintained leanings in the direction of materialism. Russell observed that in denying the methodological relevance of introspection and maintaining that "psychology should only concern itself with what can be seen by external observation," the behaviorist school ultimately reduces all psychological phenomena to physical phenomena, "thereby conceding to materialism the utmost of its claims."[11]

Lange took this charge further and contended that political economy, too, has tended to rely upon a "special theory of ego-

---

[10] Bertrand Russell, introduction to *The History of Materialism and Criticism of Its Present Importance*, by F. A. Lange, trans. Ernest Chester Thomas, 3rd ed., 3 vols. in one (London: Routledge & Kegan Paul, 1925), 1:xii. The first German edition of Lange's work was published in 1865 and published in translation in English in three volumes in 1877, 1890, and 1892. The English text was reissued as three volumes in one in 1925 (reprinted in 1950 and 1957) as part of the International Library of Psychology, Philosophy and Scientific Method published by Routledge & Kegan Paul. All citations are to the 1925 edition.

[11] Russell, introduction to *History of Materialism*, 1:xviii.

ism, which more than any other element of modern times bears on it the stamp of Materialism."[12] Lange points us back to Adam Smith, whose *An Inquiry Into the Nature and Causes of the Wealth of Nations* laid the groundwork for the science of economics by identifying the mechanism of the division of labor and the laws (in the sense of regular patterns of human interaction) of supply and demand that seem to coordinate the market of interests. While Lange affirms that Adam Smith, who was also the author of *The Theory of Moral Sentiments*, never confounded the operation of the market of interests with the whole of life, he observes that his successors, "forgot the other side, and confounded the rules of the market with the rules of life; nay, even with the elementary laws of human nature." The result was that political economy, by simplifying the problems of human intercourse to the operation of the newly discovered economic "laws," took on the appearance of "strict science."[13] In Lange's assessment this simplification mired political economy in ethical egoism, an atomistic conception of society, and ultimately a complicated relationship with Christian ethics.

On the one hand, the revulsion of many nineteenth-century scholars to the implications of such ethical egoism, and, on the other hand, the rise of a new "positive" social science that repudiated metaphysics and theism, ushered in challenges to classical *laissez faire* economics, which had begun to discover the undesigned patterns of order that could arise from transactional economic and social interactions. Breaking from the older moral philosophy that they began to replace, the new social scientists sought to examine psychological and social structures and their origins and functions. Such moves helped increasingly pit religion against science and the church against the state. The new "religion of humanity" prescribed by Auguste Comte sought to

---

[12] Lange, *History of Materialism*, 3:233.

[13] Lange, *History of Materialism*, 3:235.

translate the older structure of the church into a new positivist key, and "society" became both an object of veneration and the primary source of collective virtue and beneficence.

In his 2001 book, *Economics as Religion*, economist Robert Nelson recounted the ways in which economics came to operate in society with its own religion-like structure. Nelson argues that modern economics has operated in many ways as a secularized version of Protestant theology in which the primary evil is economic scarcity and in which deliverance from this evil (and the attainment of heaven on earth) will come through application of economic science to promote efficiency (and fairness) in production and distribution. In this worldview, economists, as technical advisors to governmental managers, serve as a new "scientific" priesthood effecting a secular salvation of human society through the application of constructivist reason, the sort of reasoning that seeks to deliberately design choices and institutions to generate what are perceived as "optimal" outcomes.[14]

Here, then, within the very discipline to which Vernon Smith has devoted his life's work, there seems to be a persistent tendency if not to outright materialism then to a reduction of human rationality within constructivist constraints. As Smith acknowledges, "predominately, both economists and psychologists are reluctant to allow that naïve and unsophisticated agents can achieve socially optimal ends without a comprehensive understanding of the whole, as well as their individual parts, implemented by deliberate action. There is no 'magic.'"[15] For over a century the classical rationale for free markets has encountered

---

[14] Robert H. Nelson, *Economics as Religion: From Samuelson to Chicago and Beyond* (University Park: Pennsylvania State University Press, 2001), xv.

[15] Vernon L. Smith, *Rationality in Economics: Constructivist and Ecological Forms* (Cambridge: Cambridge University Press, 2008), 157.

methodological, ethical, and theological challenges that economists have been hard pressed to address from within what Smith calls the standard social science model (SSSM).[16] Economists, much more so than theoretical physicists, however, wield social influence that helps shape the beliefs that govern economic and social policy and do, in fact, act as a sort of priesthood to the modern state. It could thus be as important for those interested in exploring the ongoing viability of Christian belief and practice in the modern world to understand the faith of Vernon Smith the economist as the faith of Vernon Smith the student of physics.

It is on this front where Smith's address leaves me wanting more. Unfortunately, Smith does not develop his thoughts with the philosophical depth attempted by his fellow economist Robert Nelson, whose 2015 book, *God? Very Probably: Five Rational Ways to Think about the Question of a God*, explicitly states one of the challenges with which people of faith must be concerned, namely that "in the twentieth century, the social sciences displaced traditional Jewish and Christian theology as the most authoritative way of thinking about the human condition in society and the world."[17] This displacement, however, has largely left us with tools inadequate to the task of understanding the human condition. As Nelson observes:

> Regarding the physical sciences as the highest form of learning, economists and other social scientists since World War II have devised various mathematical modeling, statistical and other formal quantitative meth-

---

[16] Vernon L. Smith. "Constructivist and Ecological Rationality in Economics," Nobel Prize Lecture, December 8, 2002, 504, http://www.nobelprize.org/nobel_prizes/economic-sciences/laureates/2002/smith-lecture.pdf.

[17] Robert H. Nelson, *God? Very Probably: Five Rational Ways to Think about the Question of a God* (Eugene, OR: Cascade Books, 2015), 13.

ods in hopes of replicating the successes of physics. Unfortunately, however, this effort has mostly failed. Moreover, it is the most important questions—dealing with issues of the greatest historical and social significance—that are the least suitable for applying the formal methods of social science quantitative analysis.[18]

Nor does Smith reach as far or offer us as much theological insight as John Polkinghorne's book *The Faith of a Physicist*. In this work, Polkinghorne, a former Cambridge professor of mathematical physics and an Anglican priest, tries to explicate the grounds not merely for a simple theism but for his subscription to the orthodox Christian doctrine of the Trinity and Incarnation, taking as his outline the Nicene Creed. Polkinghorne clearly articulates the stakes of belief in God over against the belief in truths of science:

> Central to all talk of the knowledge of God is the recognition that it is not available to us on a merely speculative basis. I believe in quarks, but the acknowledgement of their existence does not touch or threaten me in my own being. It is very different with belief in God, which has consequences for all that I do and hope for.[19]

While Smith articulately defends the compatibility of faith and science on the basis of the demise of materialism, we are left with significant questions. What, for instance, might his remarks suggest to us about the unresolved problems surrounding the ethical foundations of social order, about the place of Christianity in shaping those ethical foundations, and ultimately about the phenomenon of faith itself? How would Smith explain his

---

[18] Nelson, *God? Very Probably*, 12.

[19] John Polkinghorne, *The Faith of a Physicist: Reflections of a Bottom-Up Thinker* (Princeton: Princeton University Press, 1994), 41.

faith to his "favorite atheist" Richard Dawkins, who sees faith ultimately as God delusion? Does Smith, whose work has been cutting-edge in developing the new blended fields of experimental economics and neuroeconomics, believe that the convergence of sciences (Polkinghorne might say consilience) will make room for the full fabric of orthodox theological belief?

Most importantly, I believe one is left with the question of how Smith's own work to understand the existence and operation of what he calls ecological rationality, in contrast to the constructivist rationality that has been primary in giving shape to the modern "public-private partnership" between social science and the administrative welfare state, might help shape a philosophical anthropology that makes human beings out to be unique, dignity-bearing, moral persons capable of response to the call of God.

In *Desiring the Kingdom: Worship, Worldview, and Cultural Formation*, theologian James K. A. Smith argues that neither the person-as-thinker model of rationalist philosophy nor the person-as-believer model of contemporary "worldview" theology, provide a sufficient account of man's nature. Instead, Smith (J. K. A.) offers a philosophical anthropology based on an intentional account of human persons. People, in essence, are thinking and believing, but beneath these things they are desiring creatures.

> The "desiring" model of the human person begins from our nature as intentional beings who first and foremost (and ultimately) intend the world in the mode of *love*. We are primordially and essentially agents of love, which takes the structure of desire of longing. We are essentially and ultimately desiring animals, which is simply to say

> that we are essentially and ultimately lovers. To be human
> is to love, and it is what we love that defines who we are.[20]

Working from desire and intention, human persons must be modeled in a dynamic rather than static manner. Modeling human societies thus becomes an even more complex problem that can be only inadequately represented through modern statistical snapshots, for people are always embedded in a dynamic nexus of social relationships and cultural institutions.[21] Smith (J. K. A.) further asserts that "there are no private practices … our hearts are constantly being formed by others, and most often through the cultural institutions that we create."[22] Smith's description of these cultural institutions here begins to resonate with the economic theorists of spontaneous order:

> So cultural institutions are those conglomerations of practices (and built-environment) that have unfolded and developed over time to address human needs, wants, and desires. These institutions don't fall from the sky ready-made; in other words, cultural institutions are not "created," they are sub-created…. They are engendered and unfolded by human creation, responding to invitations that are embedded in the earth, we might say … there is also an important sense in which cultural institutions take on a life of their own; while they are ultimately human creations, once they're up and running, they cannot be

---

[20] James K. A. Smith, *Desiring the Kingdom: Worship, Worldview, and Cultural Formation*, Cultural Liturgies, vol. 1 (Grand Rapids, MI: Baker Academic, 2009), 50–51.

[21] Theorists of the Austrian school of economics such as Ludwig von Mises, Ludwig Lachmann, and others have inspired work in this direction among a small but growing sector of economists who are, consistent with Nelson's observations about the religious structure of the economics profession, considered "heterodox."

[22] James K. A. Smith, *Desiring the Kingdom*, 71.

reduced to the particular whims and interests of particular human beings.[23]

Accounting for the operation of ecological rationality, Vernon Smith puts things this way:

> Emergent arrangements and behaviors, even if initially constructivist, must have fitness properties that incorporate opportunity costs and social environmental challenges invisible to constructivist modeling, but that are an integral part of experience and selection processes. This leads to an alternative, ecological concept of rationality: an emergent order based on trial-and-error cultural and biological coevolutionary change. These processes yield home- and socially-grown rules of action, traditions, and moral principles that underlie emergent (property) rights to act that create social cohesion in personal exchange.[24]

In this matter of the emergence of cultural institutions by human action but not necessarily human design, Polkinghorne lifts our attention back to the intersection of theoretical physics and the theology of creation. "From a theological point of view," writes Polkinghorne, "the roles of chance and necessity should be seen as reflections of the twin gifts of freedom and reliability, bestowed on his creation by One who is both loving and faithful." Not only does the emergence of cultural forms depend upon the "separate behaviours of constituents" but there is an "intrinsic unpredictability of chaotic systems [that] is to be interpreted as leaving room for the operation of top-down organizing principles." Or put another way, "Heaven is the

23 James K. A. Smith, *Desiring the Kingdom*, 71–72.
24 Smith, *Rationality in Economics*, 322.

outward completion of earth, in the direction of the open and the unknown."[25]

In revealing to us the surprising capacity of people with bounded knowledge playing in iterated exchange games to converge quickly to equilibrium prices and to apply, if often unconsciously, principles of reciprocity and fairness, sometimes at the expense of personal utility maximization, Vernon Smith's experimental economics can seem at times to be revealing a human form of "spooky action at a distance." Smith's work makes clear that the standard social scientific model cannot provide adequate explanations of these observable phenomena. Whether experimental methods will eventually yield a sufficient quantity of consistent data to support a compelling theoretical explanation of these phenomena is yet to be seen. In either case, we can and should be ready to inquire what any of our theories of human rationality and human action might imply about the ultimate reality of human nature. Theories of mind that dismiss faith as an irrational delusion fail *prima facie* to account for the very persistence of faith among many of those—such as Vernon Smith and John Polkinghorne—who have been trained in the most rigorous and critical forms of scientific reasoning.

Polkinghorne reminds us that there are limitations on theory construction in theology because of its very subject matter and the nature of its data (Scripture, tradition, and subjective religious experience). Smith's insights on ecological rationality confirm that the limitations on theory formation may also extend to the nature of human sociality itself. And yet, neither Smith nor Polkinghorne believes this leaves us paralyzed in darkness. Polkinghorne is eloquent on this point:

> The ability of understanding to outrun explanation is intimately connected with the religious concept of faith. This is not a polite expression for unsubstantiated assertion,

---

[25] Polkinghorne, *Faith of a Physicist*, 77, 80.

> but it points to an ability to grasp things in totality, the occurrence of an insight which is satisfying to the point of being self-authenticating, without dependence on detailed analysis. Involved is a leap of the mind—not into the dark, but into the light. The attainment of understanding in this way does not remove the obligation to seek subsequent explanation, to the degree that it is available, but the insight brings with it a tacit assurance that such explanation should be there for the eventual finding.[26]

Smith's experimental endeavors to find explanations for the phenomena of market exchange, which we have come to include in the category of spontaneous (or emergent) social orders, rests on a faith in the premises not only of science but also on an anthropology that recognizes "a deep human capacity to acquire tacit knowledge that defies all but fragmentary articulation in natural or written langugage."[27] It would be good to hear further conversations among the thinkers I have been seeking to draw together here, and especially to see more economists venturing into these thorny paths and reflecting on their own methodologies, the predominant liturgies of the modern economics priesthood, and the meaning of it all for our understanding of philosophical anthropology.

Perhaps a unified theory of the emergence/creation of life and human consciousness and the subsequent development of culture through processes of spontaneous ordering (human action not human design) will remain elusive. Perhaps the best we may be able to do is to accede to our intuition that an invisible hand somehow operates to enable people to discover their own faith and to find communion with one another, not merely in the fractal economies of material and cultural production and exchange but also in the Divine Economy of the Cross.

---

[26] Polkinghorne, *Faith of a Physicist*, 37.

[27] Smith, *Rationality in Economics*, xv.

Adam Smith and the Unseen: A Conversation with Vernon L. Smith*

SAMUEL GREGG. I am going to start with a question about a person that I know that you are very interested in: Adam Smith. Smith is known for his contributions to economics, but fewer people know that he was a philosopher as well and thought about metaphysical questions. How did Smith's appreciation for things unseen affect the way he thought about the world economically?

VERNON L. SMITH. Adam Smith and the other Scottish philosophers were enormously impressed by Isaac Newton. What had Isaac Newton done? He had shown that a lot of our everyday forms of experience can be accounted for by very simple laws that were invisible—invisible to our experience. But yet they could account for it. And I think much of what Adam Smith and David Hume and Adam Ferguson and others in the Scottish Enlightenment were trying to do was to work out that program for social, political, and economic phenomena. The incredible thing about the Scottish philosophers was that they were very

---

*   This interview, conducted by Samuel Gregg, Director of Research at the Acton Institute, is an edited excerpt from the question and answer session that immediately followed Vernon Smith's lecture at Acton University on June 16, 2016.

astute observers. Adam Smith was on top of details that were going on around him. Smith and the Scottish philosophers saw order in the world around them. How do you account for this order? The forces, if they existed, were not apparent. I think that very much accounts for what they were up to. Adam Smith's first book was *Theory of Moral Sentiments*, published in 1759. *Wealth of Nations* was published in 1776. There is plenty of evidence that indicates that Smith thought *Theory of Moral Sentiments* was his most important work. I think he was right. In fact, I think a lot of the misunderstanding and the distortions in people's interpretation of *Wealth of Nations* comes from the fact that they have not read *Theory of Moral Sentiments*. When Smith says that every man should be perfectly free to follow his own interest in his own way so long as he does not violate the laws of liberty, to know what those phrases mean, you have to read *Theory of Moral Sentiments*. That's where he defines what he means by following your own interest in your own way and also what the laws are that constrain us, not only in the civil order of law that we experience through governments, but also the order of rules that we follow in our intimate groupings.

GREGG. You have articulated in your presentation the limitations of the sciences—the natural sciences. In your experience, do economists understand the limitations of the science of economics?

SMITH. The way economics has developed, particularly since the neoclassical Marginal Revolution in the 1870s, is that we now think of a lot of the phenomena as a result of a conscious optimization, rational processes. Classical economics saw less intent in every action, but much more rulefollowing behavior because of the norms that we are accustomed to follow. It's what I have called ecological rationality.

Let me give you what is a fairly concrete example. The first experiments that I did were on supply and demand. What I believed, and what economists all believed in those days, was that if a market were to approach or reach the competitive equilibrium it would only be because people had full and complete information on the market. At least that was the predominant story that goes back to William Stanley Jevons writing in the 1870s. I did an experiment in which half the subjects in my class were buyers, and I gave them values. Half were sellers, and I gave them costs. And the idea is that if buyers bought below their value, they profited. So if your value is $10 and you buy for $8, you make $2, surplus. If you are a seller and your cost is $4 and you sell for $7, you make $3. I ran that experiment where everyone had strictly private information, but I did allow people to repeat. It was a two-sided, double auction. This converged to the competitive equilibrium very quickly. Well, I thought there was something wrong with the experiment. And in fact, those experiments were difficult to publish because others thought there must be something wrong.

The whole problem was that we were not accustomed to thinking in terms of process. We were thinking in terms of equilibrium and information for the equilibrium. And the neat thing about Adam Smith is that he does not start with any kind of an equilibrium notion. He starts with, first, property rights in *Wealth of Nations* (and he has told you where those come from in the previous book, *Theory of Moral Sentiments*), and then he adds a simple axiom to that, the propensity to truck, barter, and exchange one thing for another. He does not know where that comes from, other than it is an aspect of our sociability. Well, if people have a propensity to trade, what happens? You get prices. As soon as you have prices, people can start to make comparisons and calculations. They begin to make adjustments. So, for instance, people decide to grow more corn and raise fewer hogs. And so specialization is something that is discovered.

It is not something that is already out there. The problem is to aggregate the information through markets to realize that specialization. It is something that is discovered on the ground day by day and month by month.

That's the story according to Adam Smith. Well, that's exactly what my subjects in my experiments were doing. Game theorists were dumbfounded. On their understanding, if you have no information, no one should move first; you should wait. So they couldn't account for it. That way of thinking is entirely changed now, but it just shows you the difficulty we have sometimes of overcoming our way of thinking. We project that way of thinking into what we expect to be in the observations. The neat thing about the Scottish Enlightenment is that those writers were doing it the other way around.

GREGG. As we witness many scientists attempting to divorce God from reason, or God from science, do you see an about face occurring in the future and some sort of remarriage of the two?

SMITH. Oh, yes. I think it's already happening. I think more and more scientists, astronomers, and physicists are realizing the limitations of explaining the world as we now understand it in the absence of any external agency. But I think there is more and more a realization that you cannot just slough it off with, "Well, it's in my material brain." That's a cop-out. We need to hold their feet to the fire and ask them, "What do you mean by that?" And, "What's the scientific evidence?" You can't find it. Science itself has come that full circle, and I think that sets the stage for a new understanding.

GREGG. So it's not a God-of-the-gaps understanding. It's something different?

SMITH. Yes. Science is about how things work. It does not really tell you anything about purpose. We keep getting better on how things work. But that doesn't help with that other question. If you discount and refuse to accept any notion that, as humans, we have other experiences that we call spiritual or so forth—if those are not even admissible—then you know they are insisting that the gap must always be there. But I think our job is to push into that gap.

GREGG. Natural scientists often scoff at the social sciences because they say social science lacks certainty, with certainty being supposed to be the hallmark of science. Can you give an example of economic science uncovering the spooky or the nonmaterial in the process of asking something about what you have highlighted as a real hallmark of science? Is there something that economics can reveal that is spooky that the natural sciences would not naturally come to?

SMITH. There is a certain sense in which all of our discoveries that are a surprise and completely unexpected have kind of a spooky quality. One instance is the fact that people so easily reach supply and demand equilibria. Then I think of the discoveries in the 1980s, when we discovered quite unexpectedly that it is quite easy to produce asset bubbles in the laboratory. We were starting with conditions where you would not get a bubble. That was the belief. But we were getting these bubbles unaccountably. It just violated common sense that you are giving people complete information on the asset value, but they are not trading on the basis of that information. Eventually they do when they get enough experience, because you see getting to the equilibrium was an experiential thing, it was not a matter of taking the information they are given by the economists and incorporating that into their behavior. Now, those are all gaps, perhaps not really good examples, but at least they were unaccountable kinds of things at first. It requires you to reexamine what it is you thought you knew about the connection between information and rational behavior.

GREGG. How much does philosophical materialism limit economics and its progress?

SMITH. I think we have put a lot of emphasis on, of course, material wellbeing. By human economic betterment we mean material betterment. That's economic enterprise, and that's what Adam Smith worked out in his second book. But the first book had to do with human social betterment—all the things we do to make our lives better because we grow up in a social world. We learn in growing up that some actions are hurtful to others and they resent it, and some actions are beneficial to others, and they feel good about that and they tend to reward the beneficial actions. Those two sources account for a lot of the norms that we live by. Also, Adam Smith understood that—and I think this is remarkable—he understood that the downside was potentially far greater than the upside. So there is a fundamental asymmetry between gain and loss. And he didn't just postulate that; he derived it from the idea that there is an asymmetry between our joy and our sorrow. He got it from more fundamental considerations. Psychologists did not discover that until some 150 to 200 years later. Now, it's true that you go back and read an early work like Smith's that's so rich, and it's easy to read into it a lot of things that you might not think Smith actually saw. But I'm impressed by how much vision there was in that work and how much he was able to explain with it. And all of that is not about our economic world; it's about the human world of day-to-day interaction and how, when that goes well, our lives are enormously enriched.

GREGG. Anyone who deals in the world of faith and economics is constantly having to address questions about self-interest. What is self-interest, properly understood?

SMITH. Well, it means that the individual prefers more to less. In terms of a traditional kind of utility theory, it means that the subjective value, say, of something like money is monotone increasing. You are worse off if you get less of it, better off if you get more of it. Now, Adam Smith in *Theory of Moral Sentiments* says that we are all self-loving. There are several places where he discusses that. He is referring to that notion that we always prefer more to less. But, as Adam Smith says, you cannot look mankind in your face and infer that you use that principle in all your decision-making. His point is that although we are all self-loving, in the process of maturation, of growing up in a social world, we are led to modify our decisions to take into account others, so that, as he says, we humble the self-interest and bring it down to what other people will go along with. So there is never a denial of the self-interest. If in an experiment in which I can take an action in which you are better off—you get more money and I get less—how do we know that more is better for someone else and less is worse? It's because we have common knowledge of that. So in other words, being self-interested is necessary in order to know that when you take an action it can be hurtful to someone else. If you didn't have that, then you wouldn't know whether a particular action was hurtful or beneficial. And so our social groups are all about the modification of that consideration and the choices we make, so that in our intimate groupings we are other-regarding in our decisions.

GREGG. I notice you did not use the word *greed* in that answer. When many people hear "self-interest," they think "greed." So are you suggesting that a Smithian approach actually has nothing to do with greed at all when it comes to self-interest properly understood?

SMITH. It's not a matter of greed. It's a matter of, as Smith says, the individual being fitter than anyone else to take care of himself or herself in terms of knowing what he or she wants and in making judgments about that. And so, knowing that other people are also self-interested, I know what action I take would be hurtful to them. And then I take that into account. In other words, being self-interested is an input to our socializing process. There are many experimental economists and behavioral economists who want to explain that with utility function, so that if I am other-regarding, it's because I am taking into account your reward as well as mine. Adam Smith says no. Adam Smith is right. It is not in the utility function. That's the difference between an emphasis on outcomes and process. We have gotten into the habit of trying to find a utility function to explain whatever happens. And I think there are all kinds of contradictions you get into if you try to explain with utility function our sociability at the level of families, extended families, neighbors, and small groups. In our actions we assume everyone is self-interested, and then we take into account the hurts and benefits in order to get along with our neighbors. That's the model.

GREGG. What do you think is the most significant thing that people of faith can offer to the world of economic science?

SMITH. It's that virtue must be part of the way we approach everything. In Adam Smith, virtue was self-command. The idea is that in maturation, people are always marking. When we cross their space, they are marking to us what they resent or the things that they like. We learn, then, these forms of virtue that all have Christian roots. In a time of chaos and violence and evil the ultimate answers to our society's problems must come down to individuals and their moral responsibilities. Yes, it is important that there are rules of society and that our laws be consistent with that, but law only works if you enforce it. But there is no way you can enforce everything. The nice thing about a country like the United States is that you can still pick up a newspaper from in front of the drug store before the store opens and just leave the money for it. You can go to a farm vegetable stand when no one is there, see the vegetables with the prices, take your vegetables and leave your money. That's self-command.

The Evidence of Things Not Seen: An Interview with Vernon L. Smith*

Victor V. Claar. There was a big push for deregulation in the late 1970s and early 1980s in the United States. Are there parts of the economy today that you think could benefit from deregulation?

Vernon L. Smith. That movement had an impact on experimental economics and vice versa. Under President Carter, the Civil Aeronautics Board, supported by a bipartisan consensus in Congress, moved to deregulate the airlines. The airlines would be much freer to price tickets and choose their routes. But airport runway rights (landing and takeoff time slots) would still be assigned by regulation. We proposed that such rights be exchanged via a combinatorial auction procedure under which the airlines would bid for packages of rights coordinated with their choice of routes. The idea was to match the technological need to coordinate runway use rights across airports to support the choice or route schedule, and hence create a market that facilitated airline planning and decision-making.

---

*   This interview was conducted by Victor V. Claar on June 17, 2016, the day after Vernon Smith's lecture at Acton University. It originally appeared in *Religion & Liberty* 26, no. 4 (2016): 3, 12–13. Victor Claar is associate professor of economics at Florida Gulf Coast University in Fort Myers, where he holds the BB&T Distinguished Professorship in Free Enterprise

These were events that I would never have anticipated. In the 1980s, we followed up that insightful experience by developing and testing smart computer-assisted market applications for gas pipelines and electric power. Our pipeline experiments led to a liberalization of the rules under gas deregulation by the Reagan administration. Our electricity experiments led to our involvement in the liberalization of the electric power industry in New Zealand and Australia in the 1990s.

This work was especially exciting in electric power because people didn't believe that particular industry could be organized around markets. Outside the United States, power systems were dominated by government ownership, but structure was being challenged by their poor performance. This is why electricity market liberalization was being considered seriously outside the United States but not here. Foreign treasuries were hurting because their electric power industries were inefficient and unprofitable. Thatcher sold denationalization on the grounds that it would help the British Treasury. And so you had a trend toward "privatization" in countries like the United Kingdom, Chile, Australia, and New Zealand. Even where a lot of the assets continued to be publicly owned, they nevertheless had to survive using what they earned in the market. That was an important new source of discipline of the industry.

More deregulation of electric power is badly needed in the US, but that won't happen easily because electricity is regulated by the individual states. It is actually quite open and competitive at the wholesale level. But that's governed by the Federal Energy Regulatory Commission, which has been open to more use of competition and markets in the interstate transfer of power on the national high-voltage grid.

Only Texas has moved to deregulating the local retail sector, opening it up to entry and competition. Basically the need is to separate the "wires business" from the competitive delivery of energy. When you rent a car, you are not required to buy your fuel energy from the car rental company.

The car rental and the gasoline do not have to be tie-in sales. But under state regulation of electric power, the pricing of energy and the rental of the essential capital are tie-in sales; similarly, in natural gas you have to buy the gas from the company you rent the local pipes from, not from one of the many competing suppliers of the natural gas commodity. Most consumers believe that because prices in these industries are state regulated they are protected from the "evils of capitalism." It is just the opposite, but both the regulators and the companies regulated have powerful incentives to nourish that misbelief.

CLAAR. Looking back, what do you consider to be the main things we've learned from economic experiments?

SMITH. We found that our experimental markets worked very effectively, far better than anyone expected. There are two fundamentally different kinds of markets. One is a market where you buy only to consume. The trades are final. People don't buy hamburgers or haircuts to resell them or stockpile them for some future date. Most of the economy, over two-thirds of GDP, consists of nondurable goods and services like hamburgers, haircuts, and hotel rooms. Consumers rent hotel rooms to stay in them—not to resell them for somebody else to use or resell. The same thing is true with transportation services. This explains the spectacular success of transportation deregulation—airlines, railroads, trucking in the US, and electric power in many foreign countries.

The second kind of market is for goods that are durable, like houses, or intermediate items like securities. For goods that can be retraded, there is a tension between value in and value in resale. Houses last a very long time and you buy them largely with other people's money. That sets the stage for bubbles, for a divergence between value in use and value in market resale value—a divergence that is not sustainable but can sometimes be fueled for many years by the flow of mortgage money.

My original experiments in the 1950s and '60s involved supply and demand in markets for nondurable goods and services, although I didn't think of them that way at the time. It wasn't until much later, looking back, that I began to see critical features and differences that I hadn't seen before. I did not originally understand important differences between things that could be retraded and those that could not. But the markets for non-retradeable items, from the beginning, worked astonishingly well compared to what we had expected.

Think of it: People with completely private information, knowing nothing about the overall market conditions of supply and demand, found the predicted equilibrium in every one of those markets by trial and error adaptation. There were simple forms of it and very complex forms of it like electric power.

But you heard none of that story from the economic theory of the time that I and others were raised on. In fact, you learned the opposite. It was widely taught and believed that if people didn't have complete information, markets would not converge to the competitive outcome. Generations of economists were brought up believing this, and I found that very disturbing. There was nothing wrong with the mathematics, it was the thinking that was narrow.

Some people delude themselves into thinking they can manage markets better than market forces can. They try it, but it's not sustainable. That made me realize that many of the basic things we believed about economics were wrong.

CLAAR. I'd like to turn to a couple of questions that are related to your talk at Acton University. It seems like there's a disconnect between scientific inquiry and religious inquiry. And in fact, we have colleagues in our own field, economics, who are quite critical of the impact that religion has had on all forms of inquiry.

SMITH. Yes, it is a very popular attitude, which alone ought to give anyone pause.

CLAAR. Many of them make the argument that religion has at times impeded scientific discovery and progress. Yet you said there is not really any good reason for science and religion to be in conflict. Can you explain that?

SMITH. Beliefs, both religious and nonreligious, often impede science. Recent changes in the status of this conflict have occurred, but they are more a result of what has happened in science, not in religion. Science has been trying to find the ultimate reductionist building blocks of all matter, life, and energy. What science has found is that there isn't anything material there at all. The ultimate constituents are things that sometimes behave like particles and sometimes like waves. And they have modeled them with wave equations and other representations. All of these models come from scientific intuition and thinking expressed in mathematical form. You might want to ask what the observational implications of that are, but none of these things are directly observable. Nothing. The underlying reality is mystical, not material.

Robert A. Millikan was in the physics department when I was an undergraduate at Cal Tech. He had won the Nobel Prize for measuring the charge on the electron, but he did no such thing. What he did was infer the charge on the electron. He had the ability to charge an oil drop and observe its speed dropping under the force of gravity between two electrostatic plates. He can measure the speed with the electrostatic field turned off, then again with it turned on. Equations of motion allow one to calculate what must be the charge on the electron, if the change in its velocity is given by the measured change when the field is turned off versus on. But of course they are all invisible, and intangible, products of the mind. The electron is known from its theory and the effects measured by classical instruments: You infer its existence and infer its charge indirectly by mental reasoning.

CLAAR. You can observe the evidence of things you cannot see? Is that right?

SMITH. Exactly, yes; observations are indirect. It hit me years ago that in Hebrews 11:1, one finds wisdom for both science and religion: "Now faith is the substance of things hoped for, the evidence of things not seen" (KJV). In science, one must have faith in the believability, the truth value, of one's theory. Where is that coming from? You don't know it's true, but its coherence can give you a glimpse of what you can't actually lay eyes on. Then you find some controlled event that you can predict from that theory, and you can design an experiment, and the experiments all have to do with electrostatic fields and photographic plates and wires and transformers and batteries. Of course, none of that stuff had anything to do with an electron, but that's what Millikan had to set up so he could look at what happens to an oil drop and infer the implications for the charge on the electron.

You get the evidence of things not seen directly. How is that so different from what happens in religion? Science is a process for learning more and more about how things work. It tells you nothing about meaning, about purpose.

CLAAR. One of the great evangelists of the twentieth century, the Reverend Dr. Billy Graham, once said, "I've never seen the wind … I've seen the effects of the wind, but I've never seen the wind. There's a mystery to it." Was Dr. Graham on to something?

SMITH. I think that's a very good metaphor for what we're talking about. Modern science is able to devise instruments so that it is able to show that molecules of air are moving, and that's what we call wind. Billy Graham was a great American, with a powerful message for living.

I look at all this now and I see much more convergence between religion and science. I believe that reality and its recognition is going to win our allegiance if we keep our minds and hearts open. How long can Richard Dawkins keep saying, "It's in my material brain?" He's got to tell me what this material brain is that he thinks gives him so much understanding. He's claiming to know things that he cannot demonstrate. But I would say, "Wait a minute. No, don't be deceived by the language. What explains that explanation? Where is the deeper meaning?" Such superficial arguments should not deflect Christians from their belief that "Ye shall know the truth, and the truth shall make you free" (John 8:32 KJV). That includes both religious and scientific truth.

You've got to ask "Why?" like the child. I remember it most recently with my youngest son catching me up in that. He asked, "Daddy, why …?" I don't remember the question. "Why so and so?" And I said, "Well, here …" and I'm describing how things work. Then the child says, "But why? Why is that?" And so then you look for something a little more fundamental. In very few questions he's got you to the outer limit of knowledge. He's got you up against the wall, and you have no place to go because our knowledge is so limited and incomplete.

CLAAR. Some of our greatest achievements, especially in economics, go back to Scholastics like Thomas Aquinas. They wanted to understand the world around them, because, through a deeper understanding of, say, the market order, they believed they might gain greater insight into the mind of the Creator himself. Do you see in the future any sort of reconciliation of faith with scientific inquiry?

SMITH. It seems to me that they will ultimately converge. I think it's pretty neat that the Big Bang cosmologist was a Catholic priest who also was really quite an outstanding physicist. He took Einstein's general theory seriously. And in 1927, the year of my birth, he came up with the Big Bang idea two years before Eddington was able to show that the universe was expanding, which suggested a common origin or area where everything began.

Religion, like science, is all about invisible realities. And theology in religion is the analog of theory in physics.

CLAAR. For you, then, there's a real parallel between the inquiry that scientists do in the physical world and the work that theologians do in the spiritual world?

SMITH. Yes. And even in experimental economics! What are we really studying? We're studying the consequences of people having minds that result in decisions. And we can't get inside of people's minds and find out what's going on there, so we ask them to make decisions. We put them in experiments and have them make decisions, and we model that. We try to hone models that are good at explaining this or predicting that decision. But it's nevertheless an invisible reality that we can't get to. We try to infer the workings of the mind by observing its effects. That is what science does, what Millikan did. So we study the substance of things hoped for, the evidence of things not seen.

CLAAR. In your Acton University lecture, you referred to your own rebirth and baptism. Could you describe that?

SMITH. My early exposure to religion in the 1930s was defined by the prevailing materialistic agnostic interpretation of science at the time. My mother and her father had been attracted to Unitarianism before I was born. Unitarians sought to recraft their religious beliefs to embody the perspectives of science. Ultimately, I was reborn and baptized a Christian. My ever so grateful and gradual conversion process probably was accelerated by Kahlil Gibran, the wonderfully sensitive Lebanese poet, when I read his *Jesus: The Son of Man*. That right blend of sacred, secular, and mystical writings for me at that particular stage of my probing to understand became ever more meaningful in rereading. That helped me to read and appreciate Scripture that I had not been brought up on. You do not have to be brought up on it to have a sense of the spiritual. It's human, in the image of God. Maybe all roads lead to this same understanding. I hope this happens to Richard Dawkins, a very intelligent man.

Made in the USA
Middletown, DE
11 June 2024

55561961R00040